THIS JOURNAL IS ALL ABOUT

DATE OF BIRTH

TIME

GESTATIONAL AGE

WEIGHT

LENGTH

HOSPITAL(S)

EVERY *tiny* THING

Written by Trish Ringley
Cover design and Illustrations by Elizabeth Anderson

Published by Every Tiny Thing, LLC
893 Marsh Street #14905
San Luis Obispo, CA 93406
http://www.EveryTinyThing.com

Written in the USA, Designed in Great Britain, Printed in China

ISBN 978-0-9990840-1-4

Author's Note:
This book contains the opinions and ideas of its author. It is intended to provide helpful and informative material on the subjects addressed in the book. The suggestions and ideas listed in this journal are not intended as a substitute for the medical advice of your trained health professionals. All matters regarding the health of your baby or yourself require medical supervision. Consult your medical staff prior to adopting any of the suggestions in this journal, as well as any further conditions or situations that require diagnosis or medical attention.

The author and publisher specifically disclaim any liability, loss or risk arising as a consequence, directly or indirectly, of the use and application of any of the contents of this book.

OUR NICU JOURNEY

DAILY NOTES

A DAILY TRACKING JOURNAL FOR NICU PARENTS

Introduction

Coach Art Williams once famously said "I'm not telling you it's going to be easy, I'm telling you it's going to be worth it." I can't think of a more fitting bit of wisdom for NICU families, because the NICU is certainly not easy. It can be stressful, confusing, and sometimes scary. I have had the special pleasure of working as a nurse in the NICU for more than 20 years, and I have seen firsthand how challenging the experience can be for families. Over the years I have talked with countless families and helped them find practical ways to cope with the difficulties of this journey. One very helpful and popular strategy is to keep a journal.

I created this book for you and your baby. First, it is useful for keeping your baby's information organized in one place. I meant it to be a kind of informal medical record that will help you better understand developments in your baby's life.

But this book is also meant to be part family scrapbook. I hope it will remind you every day that your NICU journey is much more than statistics and numbers. Whether you're reading bedtime stories to your tiny, fragile baby who's curled up in an incubator, or spending hours just cuddling your son or daughter amidst the chaos of the hospital, I encourage you to take notice of the special ways you and your baby are bonding and growing together. This journal is a record of the first chapter in your baby's life.

Use it daily on your NICU journey to keep track of the everyday stuff, and as you look back through the days you've tracked, I hope you'll delight in seeing progress, bit by bit, towards the goal of taking your baby home. It may not be easy, but I have seen countless families make this journey successfully, and few things make my job more rewarding than seeing the joyful farewell tears and going-home smiles. Believe me, the challenges are so worth it!

~ Trish Ringley, RN

How to use your NICU journal

Any way you want! There is no right or wrong way to track your NICU experience. I suggest you take this journal with you to the NICU on the first day you have it, and show it to your nurses. Ask them to help you fill in the spaces and to explain anything you don't understand. Also, I highly recommend that you show your nurses the "What We Did Today" section and ask them when you will be able to start participating in those activities with your baby.

Whether you start journaling on day 1 or 41 of your baby's life, just open to the first daily journal page, write that number on the yellow "NICU Day #" flag, and start journaling!

After you've filled in your first 7 days of daily information, you'll find a "Thoughts of the Week" section. Here, you can write longer notes and jot down new milestones, likes & dislikes for the week.

What if there's not a place to write something you want to track?

Every NICU baby is on a unique path and there are simply too many variables to include every possible NICU item you might want to track. So improvise to make this fit your journey - it's up to you!

You can even add photos!

I've included a space each week for you to attach a photo of your baby, if you like. Each "Thoughts of the Week" page has an inspiring quote, which serves as a placeholder for a photo if you wish to add one. It can be great fun to see how your baby is growing and how the NICU equipment is changing week by week!

Need more journals?

If you need additional journals before your baby goes home, email us at JournalReorder@EveryTinyThing.com to request a discount code for your next journal.

For tips & inspiration on how to use your journal

Check out www.EveryTinyThing.com/How-To-Use-Our-NICU-Journey for sample journal pages, common NICU terms and more.

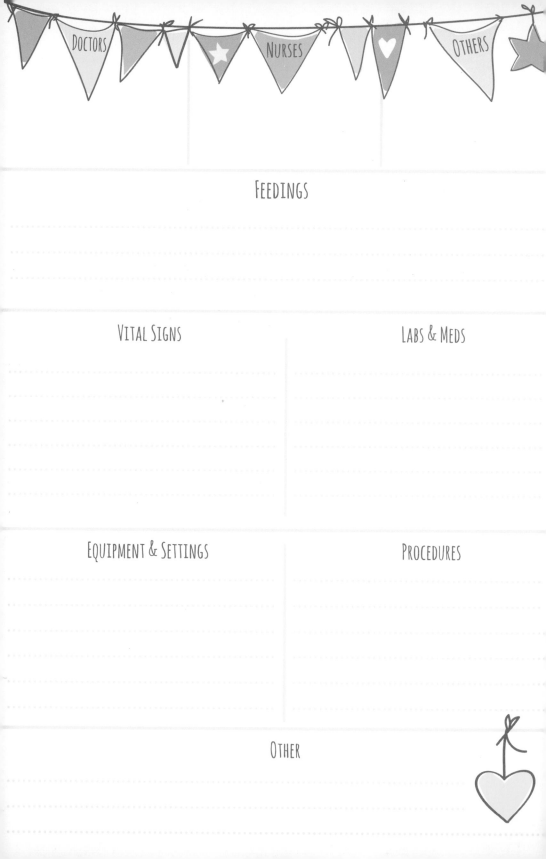

| Doctors | Nurses | Others |

Feedings

Vital Signs

Labs & Meds

Equipment & Settings

Procedures

Other

NICU DAY

Date

Gestational Age .   Weight

WHAT WE DID TODAY

PHONE CALL   TOUCH   DIAPER   HOLD   SKIN TO SKIN   CHECK TEMP.

FEEDING   READ   SING   BATH   MASSAGE   VISITORS

Ups   & Downs

NOTES & QUESTIONS TO ASK

Doctors · Nurses · Others

Feedings

Vital Signs

Labs & Meds

Equipment & Settings

Procedures

Other

NICU DAY

Date

Gestational Age   Weight

What we did today

PHONE CALL   TOUCH   DIAPER   HOLD   SKIN TO SKIN   CHECK TEMP.

FEEDING   READ   SING   BATH   MASSAGE   VISITORS

Ups   & Downs

Notes & Questions to Ask

DOCTORS **NURSES** **OTHERS**

FEEDINGS

VITAL SIGNS

LABS & MEDS

EQUIPMENT & SETTINGS

PROCEDURES

OTHER

NICU DAY

Date
....

Gestational Age
....

Weight
....

What we did today

PHONE CALL   TOUCH   DIAPER   HOLD   SKIN TO SKIN   CHECK TEMP.

FEEDING   READ   SING   BATH   MASSAGE   VISITORS

....

....

Ups .... & Downs

Notes & Questions to Ask

....

....

....

....

....

....

Doctors

Nurses

Others

Feedings

Vital Signs

Labs & Meds

Equipment & Settings

Procedures

Other

NICU DAY

Date
....

Gestational Age
....

Weight
....

What we did today

PHONE CALL TOUCH DIAPER HOLD SKIN TO SKIN CHECK TEMP.

FEEDING READ SING BATH MASSAGE VISITORS

....
....

Ups

& Downs

Notes & Questions to Ask

....
....
....
....
....
....

Doctors

Nurses

Others

Feedings

Vital Signs

Labs & Meds

Equipment & Settings

Procedures

Other

NICU DAY

Date
....

Gestational Age
....

Weight
....

What we did today

PHONE CALL   TOUCH   DIAPER   HOLD   SKIN TO SKIN   CHECK TEMP.

FEEDING   READ   SING   BATH   MASSAGE   VISITORS

....
....

Ups .... & Downs

Notes & Questions to Ask

....
....
....
....

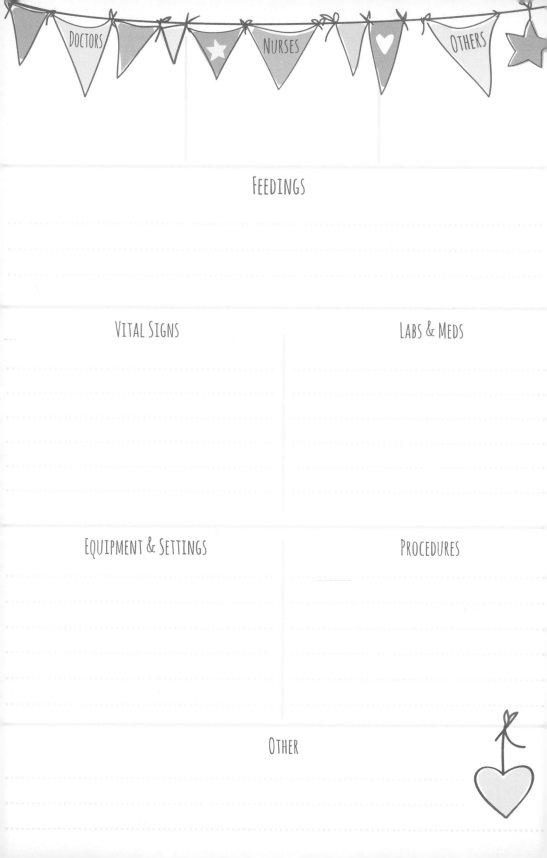

Doctors

Nurses

Others

Feedings

Vital Signs

Labs & Meds

Equipment & Settings

Procedures

Other

NICU DAY

Date

Gestational Age   Weight

What we did today

PHONE CALL   TOUCH   DIAPER   HOLD   SKIN TO SKIN   CHECK TEMP.

FEEDING   READ   SING   BATH   MASSAGE   VISITORS

Ups   & Downs

Notes & Questions to Ask

Doctors   Nurses   Others

Feedings

....
....
....

Vital Signs

....
....
....
....
....

Labs & Meds

....
....
....
....

Equipment & Settings

....
....
....
....
....

Procedures

....
....
....
....

Other

....
....

NICU DAY

Date ....

Gestational Age .... Weight ....

What we did today

PHONE CALL   TOUCH   DIAPER   HOLD   SKIN TO SKIN   CHECK TEMP.

FEEDING   READ   SING   BATH   MASSAGE   VISITORS

Ups .... & Downs

Notes & Questions to Ask

THOUGHTS OF THE WEEK

SOMETIMES THE SMALLEST THINGS TAKE
UP THE MOST ROOM IN YOUR HEART.

- A.A.MILNE

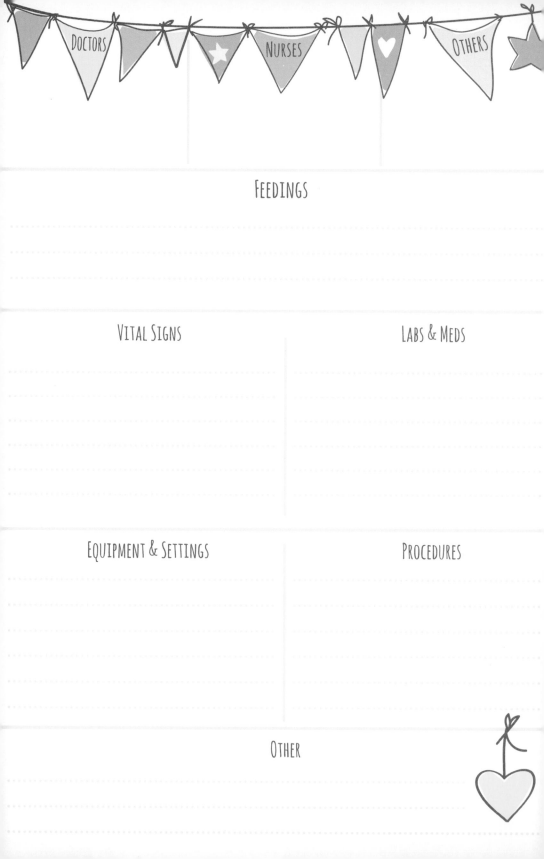

Doctors Nurses Others

Feedings

Vital Signs

Labs & Meds

Equipment & Settings

Procedures

Other

NICU DAY

Date ....

Gestational Age ....   Weight ....

What we did today

PHONE CALL   TOUCH   DIAPER   HOLD   SKIN TO SKIN   CHECK TEMP.

FEEDING   READ   SING   BATH   MASSAGE   VISITORS

Ups .... & Downs

Notes & Questions to Ask

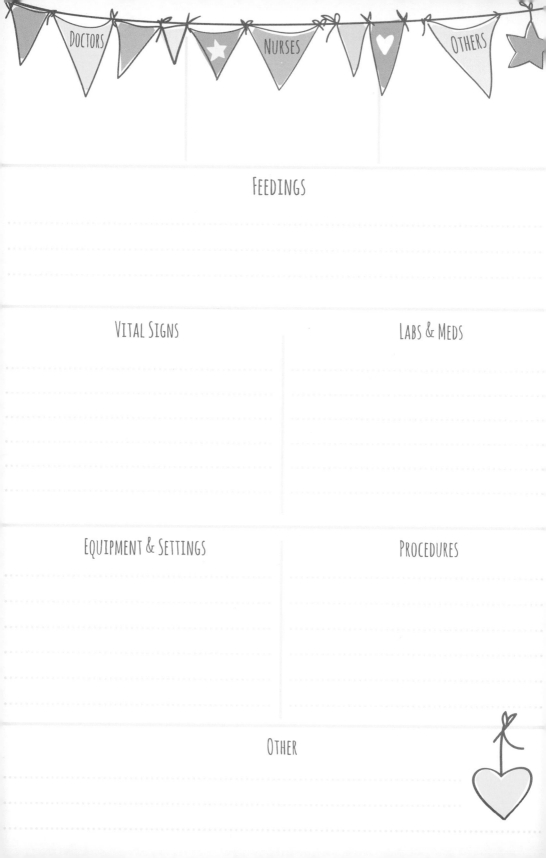

Doctors

Nurses

Others

Feedings

Vital Signs

Labs & Meds

Equipment & Settings

Procedures

Other

NICU DAY

Date

Gestational Age   Weight

WHAT WE DID TODAY

PHONE CALL	TOUCH	DIAPER
HOLD	SKIN TO SKIN	CHECK TEMP.
FEEDING	READ	SING
BATH	MASSAGE	VISITORS

Ups   & Downs

NOTES & QUESTIONS TO ASK

Doctors

Nurses

Others

Feardings

Vital Signs

Labs & Meds

Equipment & Settings

Procedures

Other

NICU DAY

Date ....

Gestational Age ....   Weight ....

What we did today

PHONE CALL   TOUCH   DIAPER   HOLD   SKIN TO SKIN   CHECK TEMP.

FEEDING   READ   SING   BATH   MASSAGE   VISITORS

 Ups

 & Downs

Notes & Questions to Ask

Doctors

Nurses

Others

Feedings

Vital Signs

Labs & Meds

Equipment & Settings

Procedures

Other

NICU DAY

Date

Gestational Age

Weight

What we did today

PHONE CALL TOUCH DIAPER HOLD SKIN TO SKIN CHECK TEMP.

FEEDING READ SING BATH MASSAGE VISITORS

Ups

& Downs

Notes & Questions to Ask

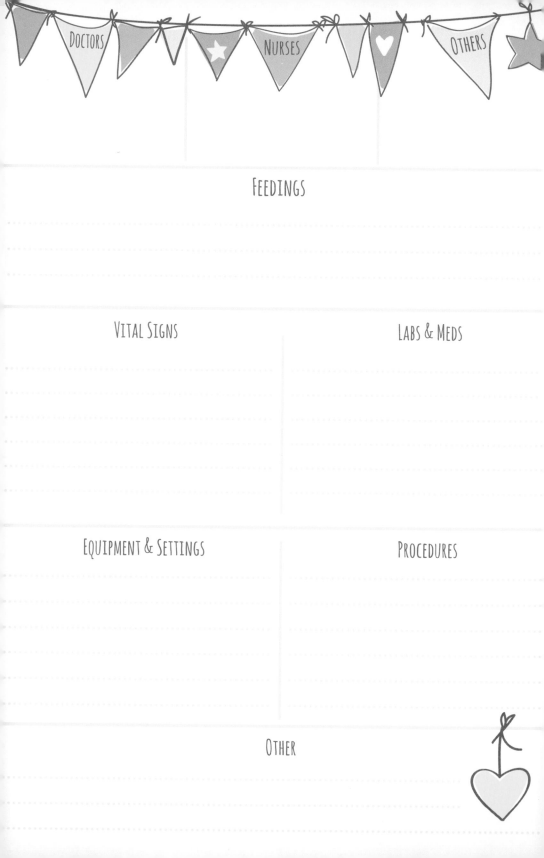

Doctors

Nurses

Others

Feedings

Vital Signs

Labs & Meds

Equipment & Settings

Procedures

Other

NICU DAY

Date

Gestational Age

Weight

WHAT WE DID TODAY

PHONE CALL · TOUCH · DIAPER · HOLD · SKIN TO SKIN · CHECK TEMP.

FEEDING · READ · SING · BATH · MASSAGE · VISITORS

Ups

& Downs

NOTES & QUESTIONS TO ASK

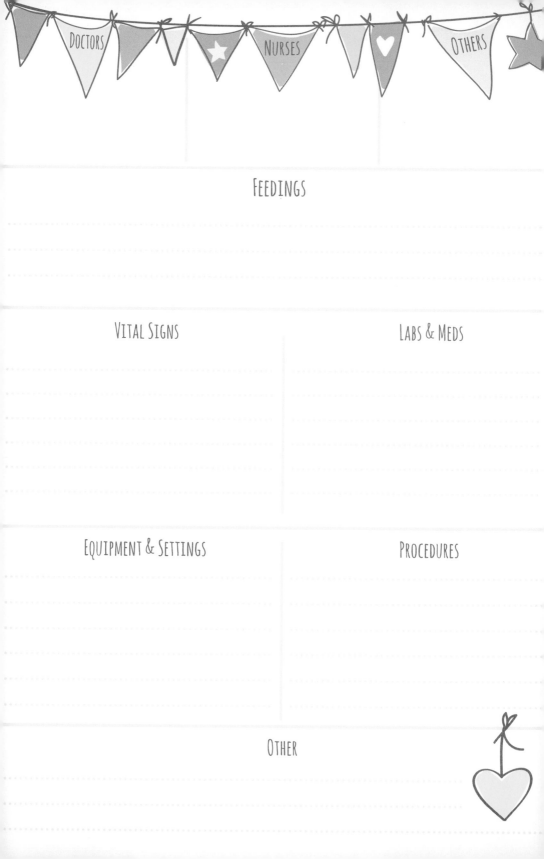

Doctors **Nurses** **Others**

Feedings

Vital Signs

Labs & Meds

Equipment & Settings

Procedures

Other

NICU DAY

Date
....

Gestational Age
....

Weight
....

WHAT WE DID TODAY

PHONE CALL   TOUCH   DIAPER   HOLD   SKIN TO SKIN   CHECK TEMP.

FEEDING   READ   SING   BATH   MASSAGE   VISITORS

Ups .... & Downs

NOTES & QUESTIONS TO ASK

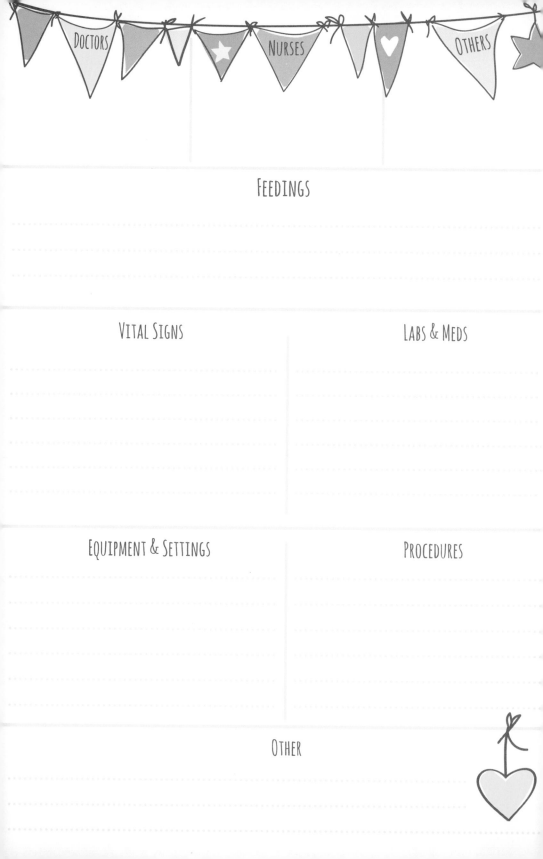

Doctors

Nurses

Others

Feedings

Vital Signs

Labs & Meds

Equipment & Settings

Procedures

Other

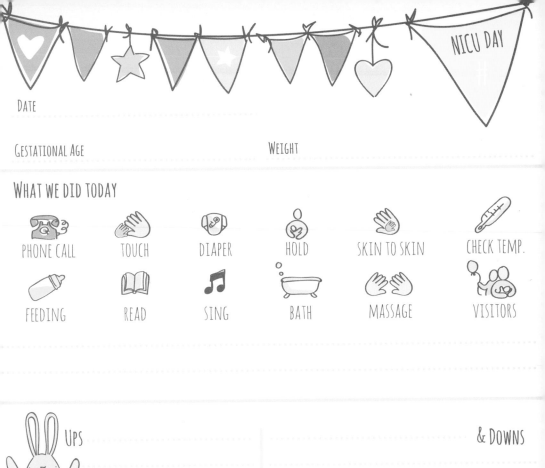

NICU DAY

Date

Gestational Age   Weight

What we did Today

PHONE CALL	TOUCH	DIAPER	HOLD	SKIN TO SKIN	CHECK TEMP.
FEEDING	READ	SING	BATH	MASSAGE	VISITORS

Ups   & Downs

Notes & Questions to Ask

THOUGHTS OF THE WEEK

LOVE

MILESTONES

BABY LIKES

BABY DISLIKES

IT ALWAYS SEEMS
IMPOSSIBLE UNTIL
IT'S DONE

- NELSON MANDELA

Doctors

Nurses

Others

Feedings

Vital Signs

Labs & Meds

Equipment & Settings

Procedures

Other

NICU DAY

Date ....

Gestational Age .... Weight ....

WHAT WE DID TODAY

PHONE CALL   TOUCH   DIAPER   HOLD   SKIN TO SKIN   CHECK TEMP.

FEEDING   READ   SING   BATH   MASSAGE   VISITORS

Ups .... & Downs

NOTES & QUESTIONS TO ASK

DOCTORS

NURSES

OTHERS

FEEDINGS

VITAL SIGNS

LABS & MEDS

EQUIPMENT & SETTINGS

PROCEDURES

OTHER

NICU DAY

Date
....

Gestational Age
....

Weight
....

WHAT WE DID TODAY

PHONE CALL   TOUCH   DIAPER   HOLD   SKIN TO SKIN   CHECK TEMP.

FEEDING   READ   SING   BATH   MASSAGE   VISITORS

Ups .... & Downs

NOTES & QUESTIONS TO ASK

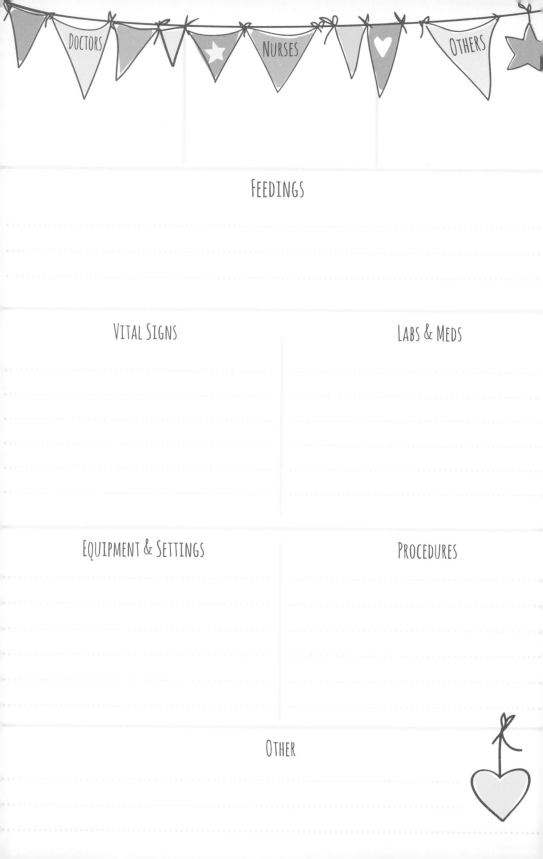

DOCTORS

NURSES

OTHERS

FEEDINGS

VITAL SIGNS

LABS & MEDS

EQUIPMENT & SETTINGS

PROCEDURES

OTHER

NICU DAY

Date

Gestational Age

Weight

WHAT WE DID TODAY

PHONE CALL   TOUCH   DIAPER   HOLD   SKIN TO SKIN   CHECK TEMP.

FEEDING   READ   SING   BATH   MASSAGE   VISITORS

Ups   & Downs

NOTES & QUESTIONS TO ASK

Doctors **Nurses** **Others**

Feedings

Vital Signs

Labs & Meds

Equipment & Settings

Procedures

Other

NICU DAY

Date

Gestational Age   Weight

WHAT WE DID TODAY

PHONE CALL   TOUCH   DIAPER   HOLD   SKIN TO SKIN   CHECK TEMP.

FEEDING   READ   SING   BATH   MASSAGE   VISITORS

Ups   & Downs

NOTES & QUESTIONS TO ASK

DOCTORS   NURSES   OTHERS

FEEDINGS

VITAL SIGNS

LABS & MEDS

EQUIPMENT & SETTINGS

PROCEDURES

OTHER

NICU DAY

DATE

GESTATIONAL AGE   WEIGHT

WHAT WE DID TODAY

PHONE CALL   TOUCH   DIAPER   HOLD   SKIN TO SKIN   CHECK TEMP.

FEEDING   READ   SING   BATH   MASSAGE   VISITORS

UPS   & DOWNS

NOTES & QUESTIONS TO ASK

DOCTORS

NURSES

OTHERS

FEEDINGS

VITAL SIGNS

LABS & MEDS

EQUIPMENT & SETTINGS

PROCEDURES

OTHER

NICU DAY

Date

Gestational Age   Weight

WHAT WE DID TODAY

PHONE CALL   TOUCH   DIAPER   HOLD   SKIN TO SKIN   CHECK TEMP.

FEEDING   READ   SING   BATH   MASSAGE   VISITORS

Ups   & Downs

NOTES & QUESTIONS TO ASK

Doctors

Nurses

Others

Feedings

Vital Signs

Labs & Meds

Equipment & Settings

Procedures

Other

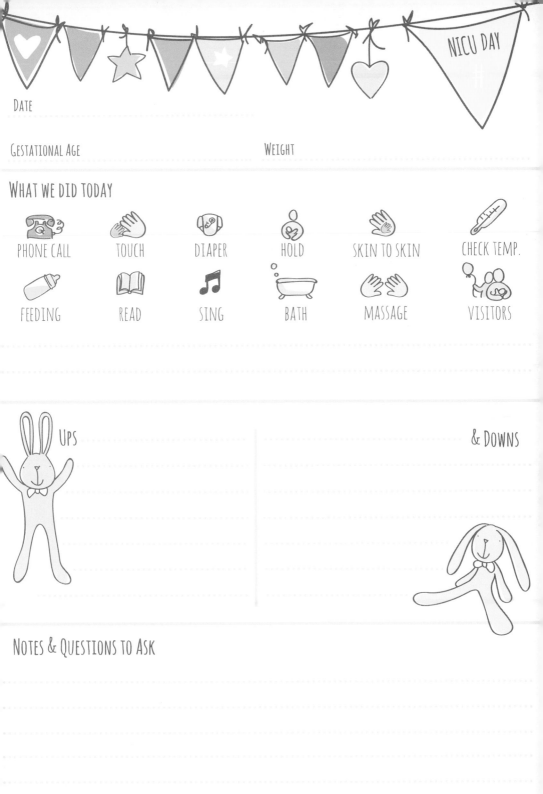

Date

Gestational Age   Weight

What we did today

PHONE CALL   TOUCH   DIAPER   HOLD   SKIN TO SKIN   CHECK TEMP.

FEEDING   READ   SING   BATH   MASSAGE   VISITORS

Ups   & Downs

Notes & Questions to Ask

THOUGHTS OF THE WEEK

LOVE

MILESTONES

BABY LIKES

BABY DISLIKES

Look for something positive in each day, even if some days you have to look a little harder.

– ANON

Doctors   Nurses   Others

Feedings

Vital Signs

Labs & Meds

Equipment & Settings

Procedures

Other

NICU DAY

Date ....

Gestational Age ....   Weight ....

What we did today

PHONE CALL   TOUCH   DIAPER   HOLD   SKIN TO SKIN   CHECK TEMP.

FEEDING   READ   SING   BATH   MASSAGE   VISITORS

Ups ....   & Downs ....

Notes & Questions to Ask

DOCTORS

NURSES

OTHERS

FEEDINGS

VITAL SIGNS

LABS & MEDS

EQUIPMENT & SETTINGS

PROCEDURES

OTHER

NICU DAY

Date

Gestational Age   Weight

WHAT WE DID TODAY

PHONE CALL   TOUCH   DIAPER   HOLD   SKIN TO SKIN   CHECK TEMP.

FEEDING   READ   SING   BATH   MASSAGE   VISITORS

Ups   & Downs

NOTES & QUESTIONS TO ASK

Doctors

Nurses

Others

Feedings

Vital Signs

Labs & Meds

Equipment & Settings

Procedures

Other

NICU DAY

Date ....

Gestational Age ....   Weight ....

What we did today

PHONE CALL   TOUCH   DIAPER   HOLD   SKIN TO SKIN   CHECK TEMP.

FEEDING   READ   SING   BATH   MASSAGE   VISITORS

 Ups ....   & Downs ....

Notes & Questions to Ask

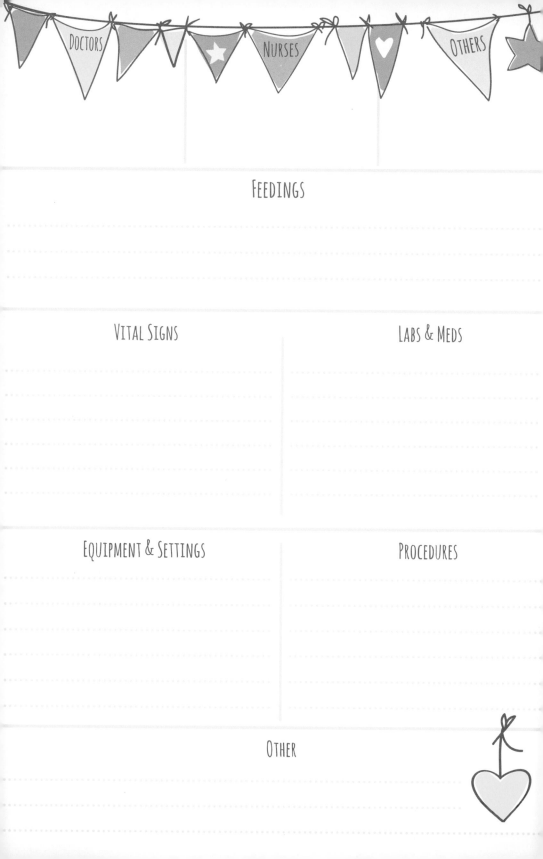

DOCTORS

NURSES

OTHERS

FEEDINGS

VITAL SIGNS

LABS & MEDS

EQUIPMENT & SETTINGS

PROCEDURES

OTHER

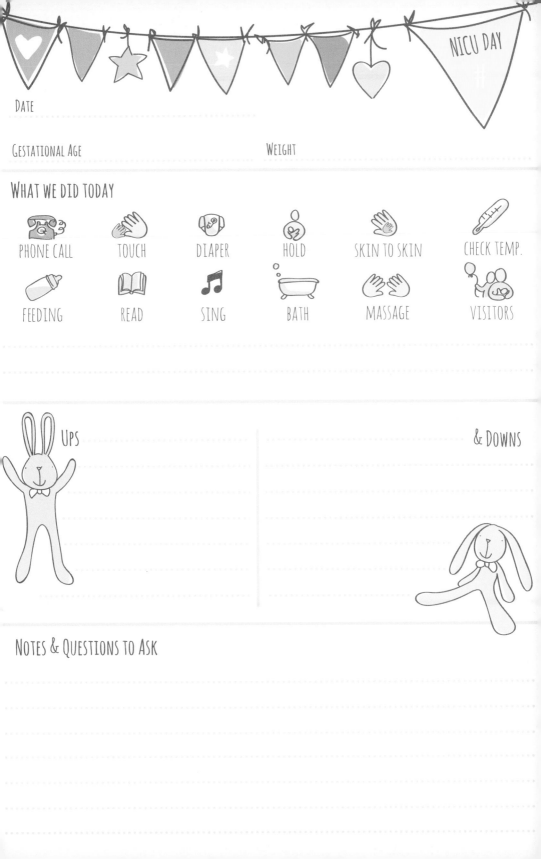

NICU DAY

Date ....

Gestational Age .... Weight ....

What we did today

PHONE CALL	TOUCH	DIAPER
HOLD	SKIN TO SKIN	CHECK TEMP.
FEEDING	READ	SING
BATH	MASSAGE	VISITORS

Ups .... & Downs

Notes & Questions to Ask

Doctors

Nurses

Others

Feedings

Vital Signs

Labs & Meds

Equipment & Settings

Procedures

Other

NICU DAY

Date . . . .

Gestational Age . . . . Weight . . . .

WHAT WE DID TODAY

| PHONE CALL | TOUCH | DIAPER | HOLD | SKIN TO SKIN | CHECK TEMP. |
| FEEDING | READ | SING | BATH | MASSAGE | VISITORS |

Ups . . . . & Downs

NOTES & QUESTIONS TO ASK

Doctors

Nurses

Others

Feedings

Vital Signs

Labs & Meds

Equipment & Settings

Procedures

Other

NICU DAY

Date

Gestational Age   Weight

What we did today

PHONE CALL   TOUCH   DIAPER   HOLD   SKIN TO SKIN   CHECK TEMP.

FEEDING   READ   SING   BATH   MASSAGE   VISITORS

Ups   & Downs

Notes & Questions to Ask

DOCTORS · NURSES · OTHERS

FEEDINGS

....
....
....

VITAL SIGNS

....
....
....
....
....
....

LABS & MEDS

....
....
....
....
....

EQUIPMENT & SETTINGS

....
....
....
....

PROCEDURES

....
....
....
....

OTHER

....
....

NICU DAY

Date

Gestational Age   Weight

WHAT WE DID TODAY

PHONE CALL   TOUCH   DIAPER   HOLD   SKIN TO SKIN   CHECK TEMP.

FEEDING   READ   SING   BATH   MASSAGE   VISITORS

Ups   & Downs

NOTES & QUESTIONS TO ASK

THOUGHTS OF THE WEEK

ALWAYS REMEMBER, YOU ARE BRAVER THAN YOU BELIEVE,
STRONGER THAN YOU SEEM AND SMARTER THAN YOU THINK.

– A.A.MILNE

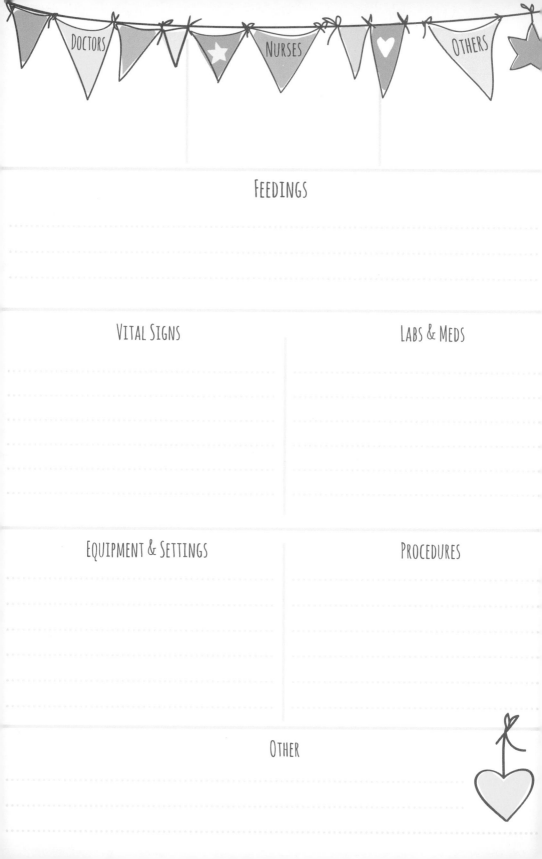

DOCTORS

NURSES

OTHERS

FEEDINGS

VITAL SIGNS

LABS & MEDS

EQUIPMENT & SETTINGS

PROCEDURES

OTHER

NICU DAY

Date

Gestational Age

Weight

What we did today

PHONE CALL	TOUCH	DIAPER	HOLD	SKIN TO SKIN	CHECK TEMP.
FEEDING	READ	SING	BATH	MASSAGE	VISITORS

Ups

& Downs

Notes & Questions to Ask

Doctors

Nurses

Others

Feedings

Vital Signs

Labs & Meds

Equipment & Settings

Procedures

Other

NICU DAY

Date

Gestational Age   Weight

WHAT WE DID TODAY

PHONE CALL   TOUCH   DIAPER   HOLD   SKIN TO SKIN   CHECK TEMP.

FEEDING   READ   SING   BATH   MASSAGE   VISITORS

Ups   & Downs

NOTES & QUESTIONS TO ASK

Doctors Nurses Others

Feedings

Vital Signs

Labs & Meds

Equipment & Settings

Procedures

Other

NICU DAY

Date
....

Gestational Age
....

Weight
....

What we did today

PHONE CALL   TOUCH   DIAPER   HOLD   SKIN TO SKIN   CHECK TEMP.

FEEDING   READ   SING   BATH   MASSAGE   VISITORS

....
....

Ups ....   & Downs

Notes & Questions to Ask

....
....
....
....
....

Doctors · Nurses · Others

Feedings

Vital Signs

Labs & Meds

Equipment & Settings

Procedures

Other

NICU DAY

Date

Gestational Age   Weight

What we did today

PHONE CALL   TOUCH   DIAPER   HOLD   SKIN TO SKIN   CHECK TEMP.

FEEDING   READ   SING   BATH   MASSAGE   VISITORS

Ups   & Downs

Notes & Questions to Ask

Doctors

Nurses

Others

Feelings

....
....
....

Vital Signs

....
....
....
....
....
....

Labs & Meds

....
....
....
....
....
....

Equipment & Settings

....
....
....
....
....

Procedures

....
....
....
....
....

Other

....
....
....

NICU DAY

Date

Gestational Age

Weight

What we did today

PHONE CALL TOUCH DIAPER HOLD SKIN TO SKIN CHECK TEMP.

FEEDING READ SING BATH MASSAGE VISITORS

Ups & Downs

Notes & Questions to Ask

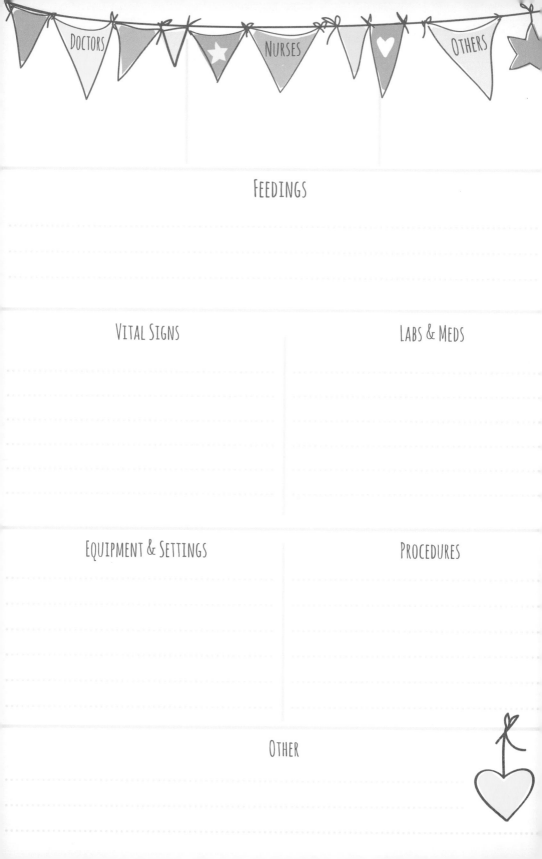

Doctors Nurses Others

Feedings

Vital Signs

Labs & Meds

Equipment & Settings

Procedures

Other

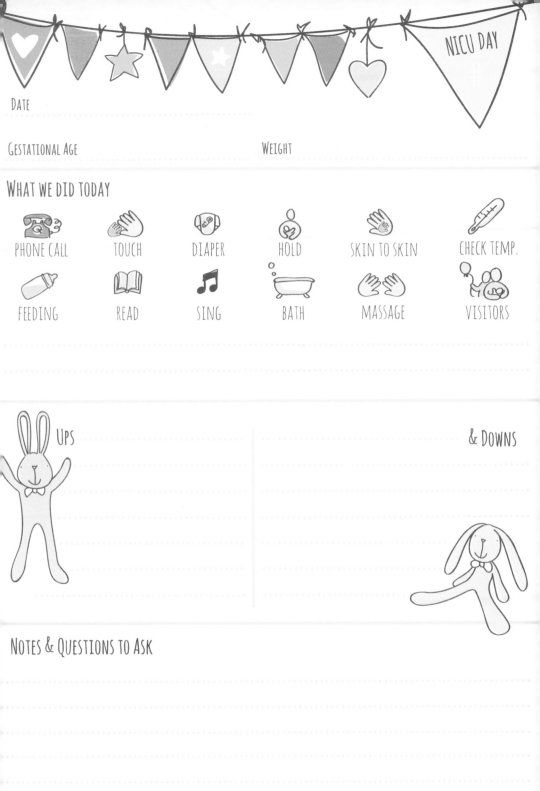

NICU DAY

Date

Gestational Age   Weight

What we did today

PHONE CALL   TOUCH   DIAPER   HOLD   SKIN TO SKIN   CHECK TEMP.

FEEDING   READ   SING   BATH   MASSAGE   VISITORS

Ups   & Downs

Notes & Questions to Ask

Doctors

Nurses

Others

Feedings

Vital Signs

Labs & Meds

Equipment & Settings

Procedures

Other

NICU DAY

Date

Gestational Age   Weight

What we did today

PHONE CALL   TOUCH   DIAPER   HOLD   SKIN TO SKIN   CHECK TEMP.

FEEDING   READ   SING   BATH   MASSAGE   VISITORS

Ups   & Downs

Notes & Questions to Ask

THOUGHTS OF THE WEEK

LOVE

MILESTONES

BABY LIKES

BABY DISLIKES

HARDSHIPS OFTEN PREPARE
ORDINARY PEOPLE FOR AN
EXTRAORDINARY DESTINY.
- C.S. LEWIS

Doctors

Nurses

Others

Feedings

Vital Signs

Labs & Meds

Equipment & Settings

Procedures

Other

NICU DAY

Date

Gestational Age

Weight

WHAT WE DID TODAY

PHONE CALL TOUCH DIAPER HOLD SKIN TO SKIN CHECK TEMP.

FEEDING READ SING BATH MASSAGE VISITORS

Ups   & Downs

NOTES & QUESTIONS TO ASK

Doctors

Nurses

Others

Feedings

Vital Signs

Labs & Meds

Equipment & Settings

Procedures

Other

NICU DAY

Date

Gestational Age

Weight

What we did today

PHONE CALL   TOUCH   DIAPER   HOLD   SKIN TO SKIN   CHECK TEMP.

FEEDING   READ   SING   BATH   MASSAGE   VISITORS

Ups

& Downs

Notes & Questions to Ask

Doctors	Nurses	Others

Feedings

Vital Signs

Labs & Meds

Equipment & Settings

Procedures

Other

Date

NICU DAY

Gestational Age   Weight

What we did today

PHONE CALL   TOUCH   DIAPER   HOLD   SKIN TO SKIN   CHECK TEMP.

FEEDING   READ   SING   BATH   MASSAGE   VISITORS

Ups   & Downs

Notes & Questions to Ask

DOCTORS

NURSES

OTHERS

FEEDINGS

VITAL SIGNS

LABS & MEDS

EQUIPMENT & SETTINGS

PROCEDURES

OTHER

NICU DAY

Date
....

Gestational Age .... Weight ....

What we did today

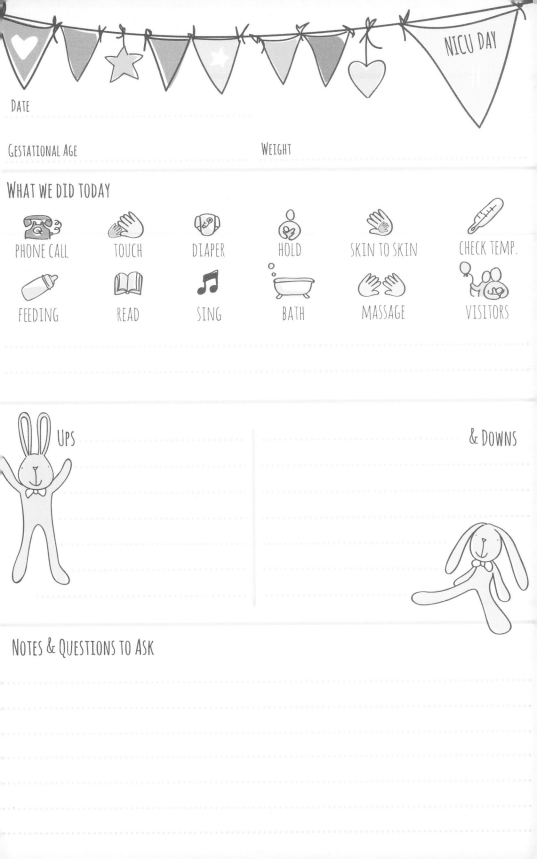

PHONE CALL   TOUCH   DIAPER   HOLD   SKIN TO SKIN   CHECK TEMP.

FEEDING   READ   SING   BATH   MASSAGE   VISITORS

Ups .... & Downs

Notes & Questions to Ask

Doctors   Nurses   Others

Feedings

Vital Signs

Labs & Meds

Equipment & Settings

Procedures

Other

NICU DAY

Date
....

Gestational Age
....

Weight
....

What we did today

PHONE CALL   TOUCH   DIAPER   HOLD   SKIN TO SKIN   CHECK TEMP.

FEEDING   READ   SING   BATH   MASSAGE   VISITORS

....

....

Ups ....   & Downs

....

....

....

....

....

Notes & Questions to Ask

....

....

....

....

....

Doctors

★

Nurses

♥

Others

★

Feedings

Vital Signs

Labs & Meds

Equipment & Settings

Procedures

Other

Date

Gestational Age   Weight

WHAT WE DID TODAY

PHONE CALL   TOUCH   DIAPER   HOLD   SKIN TO SKIN   CHECK TEMP.

FEEDING   READ   SING   BATH   MASSAGE   VISITORS

Ups   & Downs

NOTES & QUESTIONS TO ASK

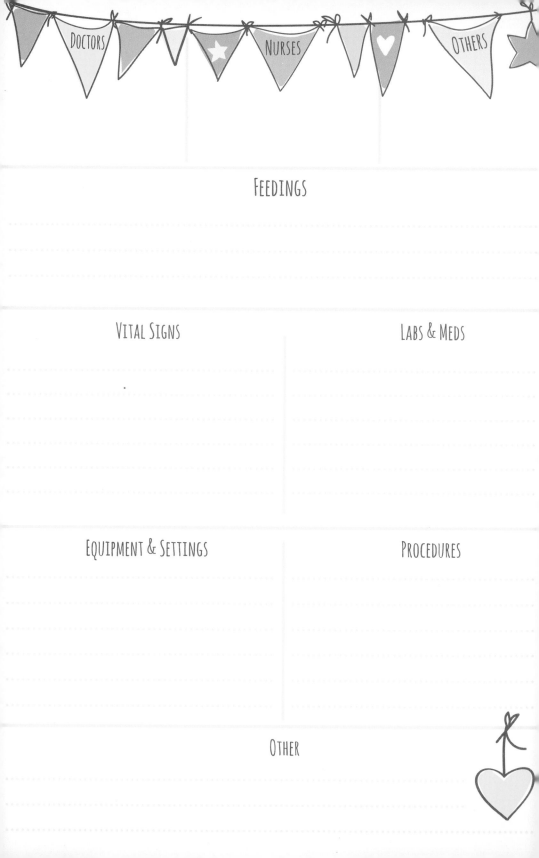

DOCTORS

NURSES

OTHERS

FEEDINGS

VITAL SIGNS

LABS & MEDS

EQUIPMENT & SETTINGS

PROCEDURES

OTHER

NICU DAY

Date

Gestational Age   Weight

What we did today

PHONE CALL   TOUCH   DIAPER   HOLD   SKIN TO SKIN   CHECK TEMP.

FEEDING   READ   SING   BATH   MASSAGE   VISITORS

Ups   & Downs

Notes & Questions to Ask

THOUGHTS OF THE WEEK

LOVE

MILESTONES

BABY
LIKES

BABY
DISLIKES

NOTHING CAN DIM THE
LIGHT THAT SHINES
FROM WITHIN

- MAYA ANGELOU

Doctors	Nurses	Others

Feeding

....
....
....

Vital Signs

....
....
....
....
....
....

Labs & Meds

....
....
....
....
....

Equipment & Settings

....
....
....
....

Procedures

....
....
....
....

Other

....
....

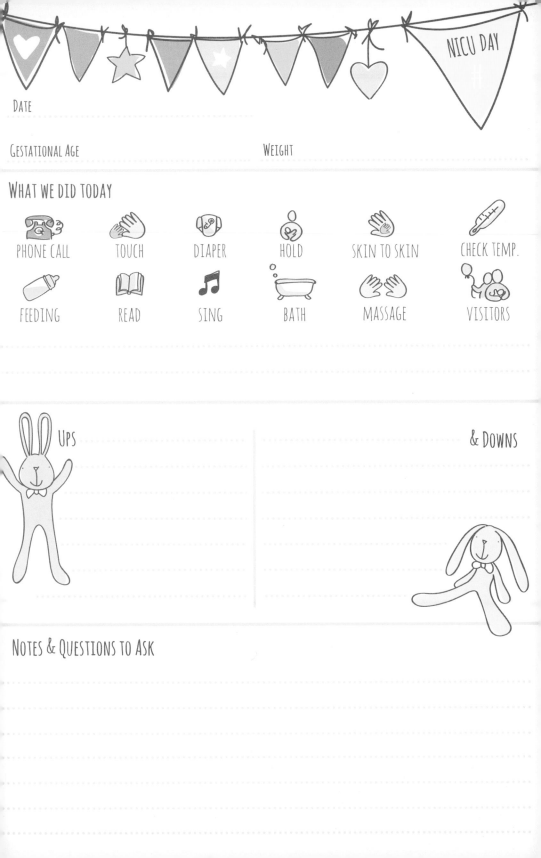

NICU DAY

Date
....

Gestational Age .... Weight ....

What we did today

PHONE CALL TOUCH DIAPER HOLD SKIN TO SKIN CHECK TEMP.

FEEDING READ SING BATH MASSAGE VISITORS

Ups .... & Downs

Notes & Questions to Ask

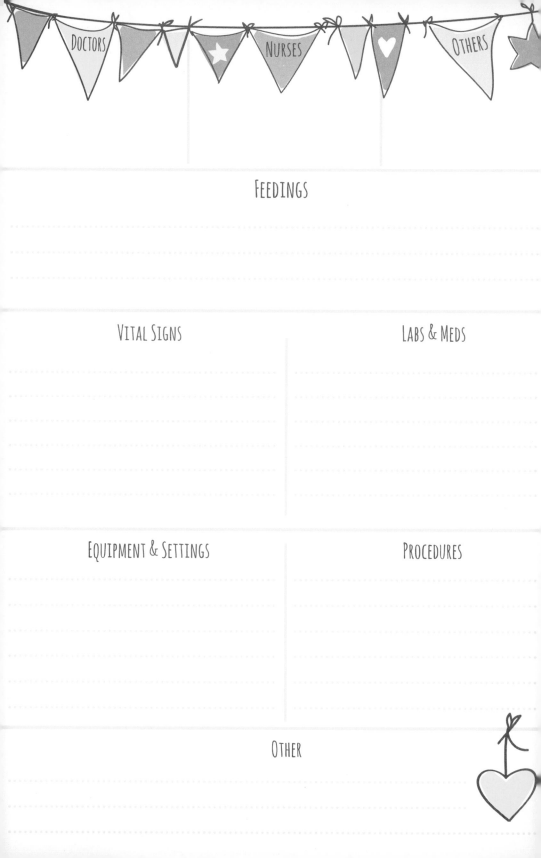

DOCTORS	NURSES	OTHERS

Feedings

....
....
....

Vital Signs

....
....
....
....
....

Labs & Meds

....
....
....
....
....

Equipment & Settings

....
....
....
....
....

Procedures

....
....
....
....

Other

....
....

NICU DAY

Date
....

Gestational Age   Weight

WHAT WE DID TODAY

PHONE CALL   TOUCH   DIAPER   HOLD   SKIN TO SKIN   CHECK TEMP.

FEEDING   READ   SING   BATH   MASSAGE   VISITORS

....

....

Ups   & Downs

NOTES & QUESTIONS TO ASK

....

....

....

....

....

Doctors

Nurses

Others

Feedings

Vital Signs

Labs & Meds

Equipment & Settings

Procedures

Other

NICU DAY

Date

Gestational Age

Weight

What we did today

PHONE CALL   TOUCH   DIAPER   HOLD   SKIN TO SKIN   CHECK TEMP.

FEEDING   READ   SING   BATH   MASSAGE   VISITORS

Ups   & Downs

Notes & Questions to Ask

DOCTORS

NURSES

OTHERS

FEEDINGS

VITAL SIGNS

LABS & MEDS

EQUIPMENT & SETTINGS

PROCEDURES

OTHER

NICU DAY

Date

Gestational Age

Weight

WHAT WE DID TODAY

PHONE CALL   TOUCH   DIAPER   HOLD   SKIN TO SKIN   CHECK TEMP.

FEEDING   READ   SING   BATH   MASSAGE   VISITORS

Ups   & Downs

NOTES & QUESTIONS TO ASK

Doctors	Nurses	Others

Feedings

....
....
....

Vital Signs

....
....
....
....
....

Labs & Meds

....
....
....
....
....

Equipment & Settings

....
....
....
....

Procedures

....
....
....
....

Other

....
....

NICU DAY

Date ....

Gestational Age .... Weight ....

What we did today

PHONE CALL   TOUCH   DIAPER   HOLD   SKIN TO SKIN   CHECK TEMP.

FEEDING   READ   SING   BATH   MASSAGE   VISITORS

Ups .... & Downs

Notes & Questions to Ask

Doctors	Nurses	Others

Feedings

Vital Signs

Labs & Meds

Equipment & Settings

Procedures

Other

NICU DAY

Date ....

Gestational Age ....   Weight ....

What we did today

PHONE CALL	TOUCH	DIAPER	HOLD	SKIN TO SKIN	CHECK TEMP.
FEEDING	READ	SING	BATH	MASSAGE	VISITORS

....
....

Ups .... & Downs

Notes & Questions to Ask

....
....
....
....
....
....

DOCTORS NURSES OTHERS

FEEDINGS

VITAL SIGNS

LABS & MEDS

EQUIPMENT & SETTINGS

PROCEDURES

OTHER

NICU DAY

Date ....

Gestational Age .... Weight ....

What we did today

PHONE CALL TOUCH DIAPER HOLD SKIN TO SKIN CHECK TEMP.

FEEDING READ SING BATH MASSAGE VISITORS

....

....

Ups .... & Downs

....

....

Notes & Questions to Ask

....

....

....

....

....

....

THOUGHTS OF THE WEEK

FROM THE TINIEST ACORN
GROWS THE MIGHTIEST TREE.

– ANON

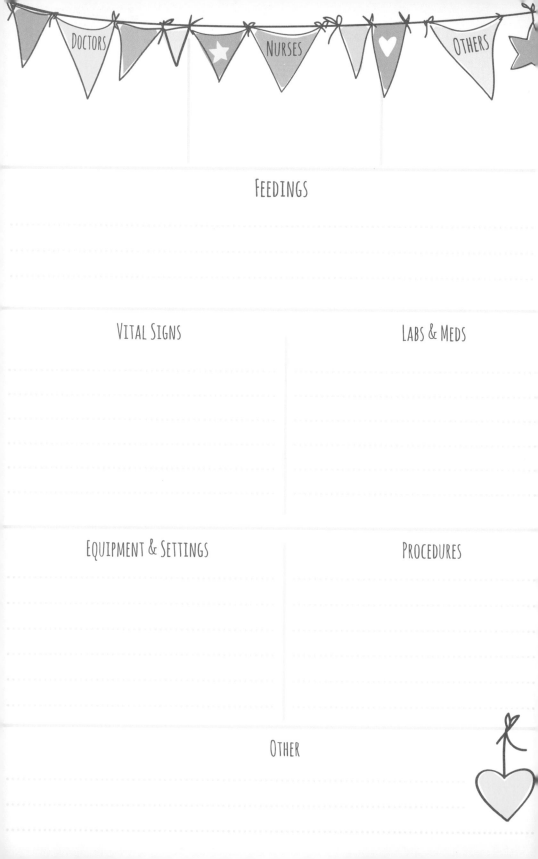

DOCTORS

NURSES

OTHERS

Feedings

Vital Signs

Labs & Meds

Equipment & Settings

Procedures

Other

NICU DAY

Date

Gestational Age   Weight

What we did today

PHONE CALL   TOUCH   DIAPER   HOLD   SKIN TO SKIN   CHECK TEMP.

FEEDING   READ   SING   BATH   MASSAGE   VISITORS

Ups   & Downs

Notes & Questions to Ask

Doctors

Nurses

Others

Feedings

Vital Signs

Labs & Meds

Equipment & Settings

Procedures

Other

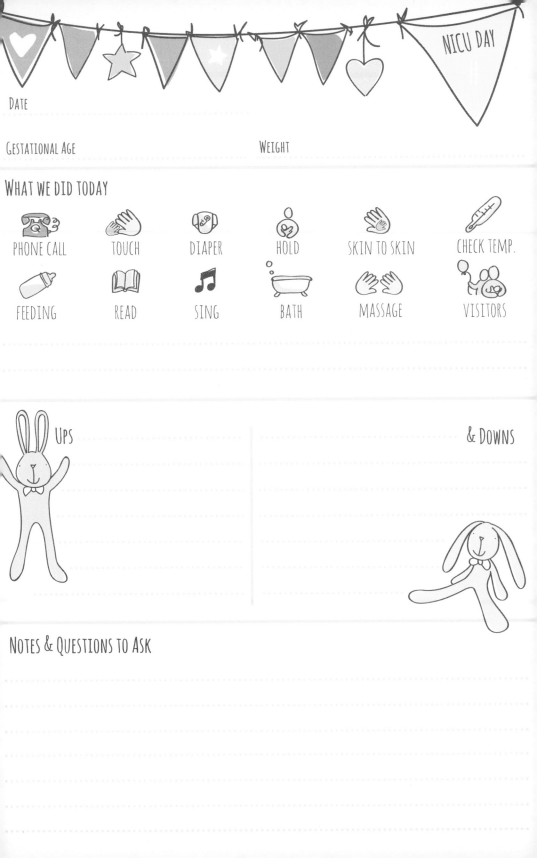

NICU DAY

Date

Gestational Age   Weight

What we did today

PHONE CALL   TOUCH   DIAPER   HOLD   SKIN TO SKIN   CHECK TEMP.

FEEDING   READ   SING   BATH   MASSAGE   VISITORS

Ups   & Downs

Notes & Questions to Ask

DOCTORS

NURSES

OTHERS

FEEDINGS

VITAL SIGNS

LABS & MEDS

EQUIPMENT & SETTINGS

PROCEDURES

OTHER

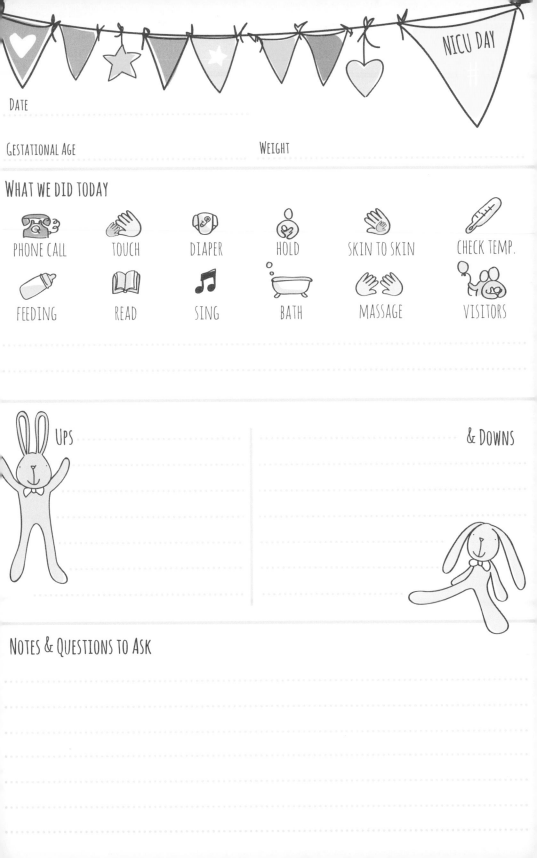

NICU DAY

Date

Gestational Age   Weight

WHAT WE DID TODAY

PHONE CALL   TOUCH   DIAPER   HOLD   SKIN TO SKIN   CHECK TEMP.

FEEDING   READ   SING   BATH   MASSAGE   VISITORS

Ups   & Downs

NOTES & QUESTIONS TO ASK

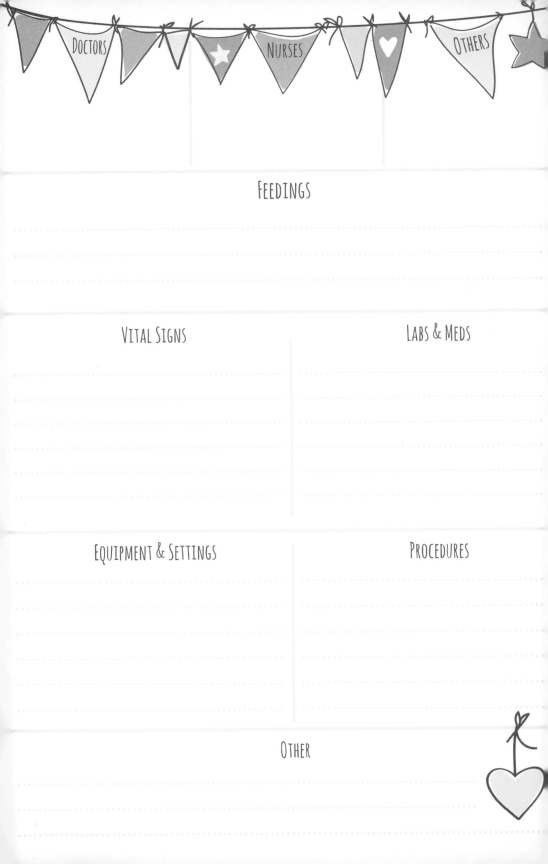

Doctors

Nurses

Others

Feedings

....

....

....

Vital Signs	Labs & Meds

Vital Signs

....

....

....

....

....

....

Labs & Meds

....

....

....

....

....

....

Equipment & Settings

....

....

....

....

....

Procedures

....

....

....

....

....

Other

....

....

....

NICU DAY

Date

Gestational Age   Weight

WHAT WE DID TODAY

PHONE CALL   TOUCH   DIAPER   HOLD   SKIN TO SKIN   CHECK TEMP.

FEEDING   READ   SING   BATH   MASSAGE   VISITORS

Ups   & Downs

NOTES & QUESTIONS TO ASK

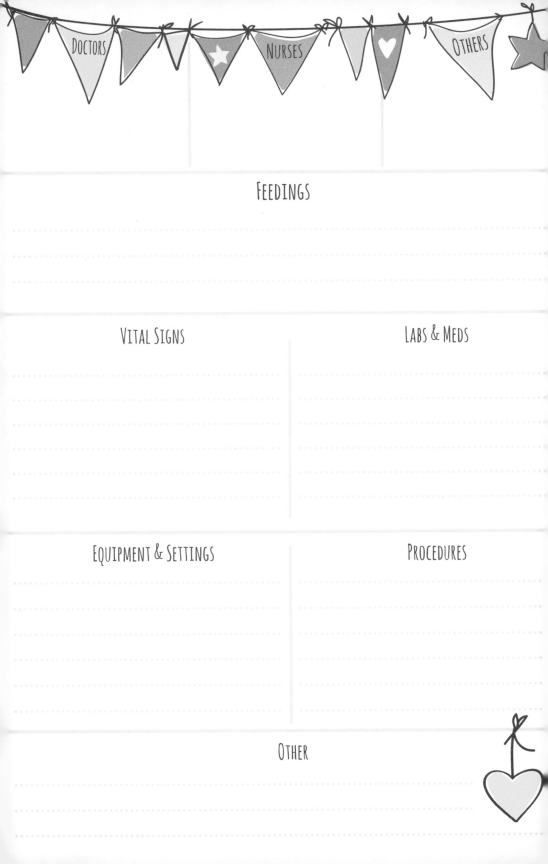

DOCTORS

NURSES

OTHERS

FEEDINGS

VITAL SIGNS

LABS & MEDS

EQUIPMENT & SETTINGS

PROCEDURES

OTHER

NICU DAY

Date

Gestational Age   Weight

What we did today

PHONE CALL   TOUCH   DIAPER   HOLD   SKIN TO SKIN   CHECK TEMP.

FEEDING   READ   SING   BATH   MASSAGE   VISITORS

Ups   & Downs

Notes & Questions to Ask

Doctors

Nurses

Others

Feedings

Vital Signs

Labs & Meds

Equipment & Settings

Procedures

Other

NICU DAY

Date

Gestational Age   Weight

What we did today

PHONE CALL   TOUCH   DIAPER   HOLD   SKIN TO SKIN   CHECK TEMP.

FEEDING   READ   SING   BATH   MASSAGE   VISITORS

Ups   & Downs

Notes & Questions to Ask

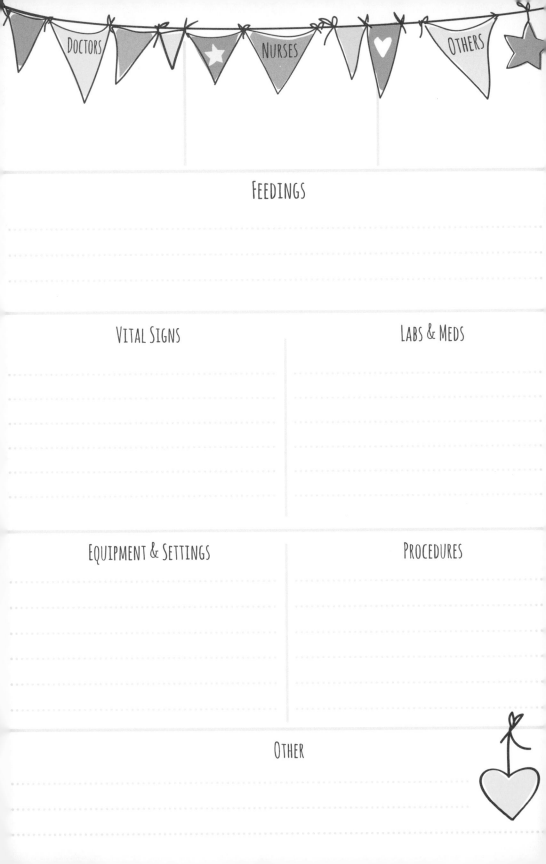

DOCTORS   NURSES   OTHERS

FEEDINGS

VITAL SIGNS

LABS & MEDS

EQUIPMENT & SETTINGS

PROCEDURES

OTHER

NICU DAY

Date ....

Gestational Age ....   Weight ....

What we did today

| PHONE CALL | TOUCH | DIAPER | HOLD | SKIN TO SKIN | CHECK TEMP. |
| FEEDING | READ | SING | BATH | MASSAGE | VISITORS |

Ups ....   & Downs

Notes & Questions to Ask

THOUGHTS OF THE WEEK

LOVE

MILESTONES

BABY LIKES

BABY DISLIKES

THE DARKEST NIGHT IS OFTEN THE
BRIDGE TO THE BRIGHTEST
TOMORROW.

- JONATHAN LOCKWOOD HUIE

FINAL THOUGHTS

Acknowledgements

This journal wouldn't be possible without the help of an incredible team of supporters. To all of my co-workers, who inspire me every day with your caring and compassion - thank you all. To the NICU parents who have tirelessly shared your wisdom and insights in order to create such a wonderful resource - this journal wouldn't be possible without you. To Elizabeth, who patiently created and modified designs that are thoughtful, comforting and beautiful - this journal is worth printing because of your talent. To my book club, for being some of the most inspiring and intelligent women I know - thanks for letting me join all those years ago! And last, but not least, a huge thank you to my family and friends, for always encouraging me and believing in me - I love you all!

HOME AT LAST

Date ....

Time ....

Gestational Age ....

Weight ....

Length ....

Days in NICU ....